the HAND of HISTORY

Born in Belfast, Ian Knox has worked as an architect, an animator and a political cartoonist. He has been editorial cartoonist for the *Irish News* since 1989, and has illustrated the weekly "If you ask me..." spot on BBC Northern Ireland's award-winning *Hearts and Minds* programme for ten years. He has also drawn for Channel 4 News, Sky News and various magazines, including *Red Weekly*, *Socialist Challenge* and *Fortnight*.

the HAND of HISTORY

as drawn by

Ian Knox

THE BREHON PRESS
BELFAST

First published 2005 by The Brehon Press Ltd
1A Bryson Street, Belfast BT5 4ES,
Northern Ireland

ISBN: 0 9544867 8 1

Design: December Publications
Printed by J H Haynes & Co Ltd

Foreword

by Susan McKay

"I have a dream!" bays Ian Paisley, arms aloft, vast jaws wide open, the teeth – those dragon's teeth – dripping saliva over his sash. "A dream that one day, every Protestant man, woman and child, no matter how ill fed, ill housed or ill educated, will one day be able to…" The speech bubble in the cartoon breaks, inviting us to explore the whole picture before continuing to read. Around the Big Man, his acolytes are showily overwhelmed by emotion. The Rev Willie McCrea is playing guitar, his plasticine mouth wide in hallelujah. Peter Robinson, obscured behind his leader, is throwing himself into a fakily enraptured copy of his style. Nigel Dodds struggles to keep up on the tambourine. A tiny Reg Empey also plays the tambourine. His eyes look nervous but his "best foot forward" little grin shows the Ulster Unionist leader is happy to be on the DUP's big bandwagon. Paisley continues, "…force a march through a Catholic street. I have a dream." Facing the politicians, the loyalist mob cheers and roars its approval. Most of the men are in dark glasses and baseball caps. A lady with a perm, in a small, church-going hat offers adoration. A rougher sort of woman holds a baby loyalist aloft. It, too, is weeping and roaring. This, from September 2005, is a classic Ian Knox cartoon.

Columnists and commentators had struggled to find words to describe the dire state of unionism after a week of loyalist mayhem on the streets. Knox nailed it. The poverty of imagination at the heart of unionism is thrown into shameful focus by the echoed words of Martin Luther King. The rabble rousing. The rabble roused, and a new generation baptised into sectarianism. As usual, with one bleak, scary and hilarious image, Knox said it all.

His cartoons are great on the day they appear in the *Irish News*: perceptive, funny – albeit often in a mirthless, Beckettian way – and provocative. But they also repay the kind of attention they can only get in a book like this. The style is so fluid, the draughtsmanship and composition so skilful, and the message so clearly and immediately conveyed that it would be easy in passing to overlook Knox's amazing artistic ability and the subtlety of his political analysis. There is no mistaking his portraits, but they are anything but static. In each cartoon his figures reveal their exact place in the political moment.

As well as providing an amazing four black-and-white cartoons a week for the paper, Knox manages a dazzling display of coloured images to illustrate the commentators featured on the BBC's fine *Hearts and Minds* programme. This is a great privilege for a writer, and Knox always enlivens the words. Sometimes, just sometimes, his cartoons seem to undermine, subtly, the commentary. He's not a man to be compromised, but he never loses his lightness of touch.

Knox is from a Protestant background, and in the best Biblical tradition, is inclined to take the mote from the eye of his own people before seeking the beam in the eye of the Catholics. Some have claimed he goes too far with his Orangutan Orangemen, their knuckles trailing the ground. Recent revelations that the most senior Orangemen don't know the difference between condoning and condemning, along with photographs of big men with Homer Simpson scarves and hate-filled faces lunging at policemen and Catholics with swords and pikes, should rest Knox's case.

Paisley is the great bête noir in his canon. His mouth is the thing – open always, like the gates of hell, blaring out some fury. Except after the Holy Cross blockade, when his mouth is sealed with sticking plaster as he hides from reporters at the House of the Martyr. Ulster Unionist defector, Jeffrey Donaldson, is seen waving a dainty farewell as he steps lightly along the way, the way being the tongue of Paisley the smiling pussy cat with a tiger's jaws.

Lately, Knox has been probing the DUP leader's personal terrors. In one 2004 cartoon he stands in front of a mirror facing a man close to death. "Take away that Romanist mirror before I sue it," he says. Journalists who had noted the 79-year-old's obvious ill health had been denounced as "Romanists".

Also in 2004, Knox has Paisley extending his hand towards the Taoiseach, Bertie Ahern, while the Paisley of winters past hurls snowballs and shouts, "Lundy". The snowballs are aimed not at the Taoiseach but at Paisley, who famously threw snowballs at Taoiseach Sean Lemass when he visited Stormont in 1965. Knox gets the full political depth of the situation. This is Paisley the self-styled outsider, the sneerer at big house unionism, accepting an invitation to come in from the cold. The invitation is offered by the head of the state he has so long denounced as hostile and evil. The doorway has scrolled pillars. This is the entrance to the marbled halls of power. A minute David Trimble is peeved to see the cartoonist observing him leaving Stormont via the cat flap.

Knox despises hypocrisy. In one of his two-frame cartoons from the start of 2005, he has the First Big Wind, Paisley blasting John de Chastelain on decommissioning: "We must have evidence." Then the second: the person almost blown away this time is Chief Constable Hugh Orde; the issue, the Northern Bank raid which he attributed to the IRA. "We don't need evidence," roars Paisley.

His Gerry Adams is a rather pompous, slightly foolish figure, terrified by the shadow of the IRA gunman, hilariously pursued by spectral Northern banknotes wailing, "We haven't gone away you know." A Knox classic followed the revelation in 2005 that the IRA had offered to kill the IRA murderers of Short Strand man, Robert McCartney. Martin McGuinness and Adams are reading the newspapers. "I mean," says an anxious McGuinness. "It would be unreasonable to expect us to sign up to a policing system that was less than perfect! Wouldn't it?" Adams ponders the question, stroking his beard. The front-page headline on his *Daily News* reads, "We'll shoot them for ye, missus."

The big Norn Iron figures haven't shifted but British secretaries of state come and go. Luckily for us and unluckily for them, Knox quickly masters a new face. Paul Murphy and John Reid are here, and the vain and self-important Peter Mandelson must have been mortified to find himself portrayed as a shyster, a self-proclaimed "short term geezer". Whether in a lawyer's wig or the cowboy hat of a Nutt's Corner dodgy dealer, he is invariably unkempt and wearing a garish tie.

Knox doesn't lacerate just the politicians with his finest nibs. He is a passionate environmentalist. His north coast bungalow dwellers are appalled: "How could anyone contemplate desecrating our coastline with an offshore windfarm?" They stare out to sea from gardens that are crushed by big picture window extensions and conservatories, and laden with coach-lamps, statues, concrete eagles and wrought iron follies. Sometimes he wrings entertainment from the dreariest situations. This is a man who attributes his intellectual rigour to the fact that he used to cartoon dialectical materialism.

He has a humanitarian's concern for the innocent victims of war. There is a devastating simplicity to the image of two gravestones, side by side. One is inscribed, "RIP Pat Finucane Not A Terrorist." The other says, "RIP Jean McConville Not an Informer."

In 1941, Robert Capa wrote as follows: "While shaving, I had a conversation with myself about the incompatibility of being a reporter and hanging on to a tender soul at the same time." Ian Knox, with his fierce wit, his well-placed anger and his compassion, shows it can be done. *The Hand of History* is a fine treatise on 21st century Northern Ireland. And it will make you laugh.

This book appears at a time of ever deepening crisis for our ancient northern land. It has never been more necessary for governments to throw millions of pounds, dollars and euros at anyone experiencing identity problems. We must rally round to protect our historic floodlit hilltop bungalows. We must cherish our top of the range German cars and our stretches of motorway leading to regional shopping malls. We must chop down trees, demolish listed buildings, hunt wildlife, abandon and abuse domestic animals. We must eat more fries, listen to more country and western music, and travel abroad to Florida, Australia and the Spanish coast. In short, we must love and save Ulster!

15.03.2000 The White House warms for Unionists as it cools for Republicans.

06.01.2001 In the first high-profile test of the new Human Rights Act, Johnny Adair is denied freedom by the Sentence Review Commission.

09.11.2002 A Catholic civil servant is arrested after police investigate alleged IRA intelligence gathering. He is released without charge, and Mark Durkan criticises "investigation by postcode".

16.11.2002 Mood music for talks. Ulster Unionists claim resuscitation of political institutions is being held back by the IRA's continuing existence and castigate Sinn Fein for not joining the Policing Board.

COMPROMISE U.S. PRESIDENT **GEORGE GORE** MEETS HIS NORTHERN IRISH COUNTERPARTS **SEAMUS TRIMBLE** AND **GERRY PAISLEY.**

IanKnox

13.11.2000 George Bush becomes President of the US with fewer votes than his rival, Al Gore. Trimble and Mallon jointly unveil a "reconciliation" sculpture at Stormont, and Paisley and Adams have yet to make a joint appearance.

19.11.2002 Following two nights of violence on the Cluan Place/Short Strand interface, Tory shadow spokesman on Northern Ireland Quentin Davies plans to spend a night with families on either side of the peaceline.

10.12.2002 The Dail introduces the British/Irish Agreement Amendment Bill, which provides for decisions in relation to the North South bodies to be taken by the British and Irish governments. Trimble threatens withdrawal from the talks.

12.02.2003 Tony Blair flies to Hillsborough for talks described by Downing Street as "significant, but not decisive" with Bertie Ahern.

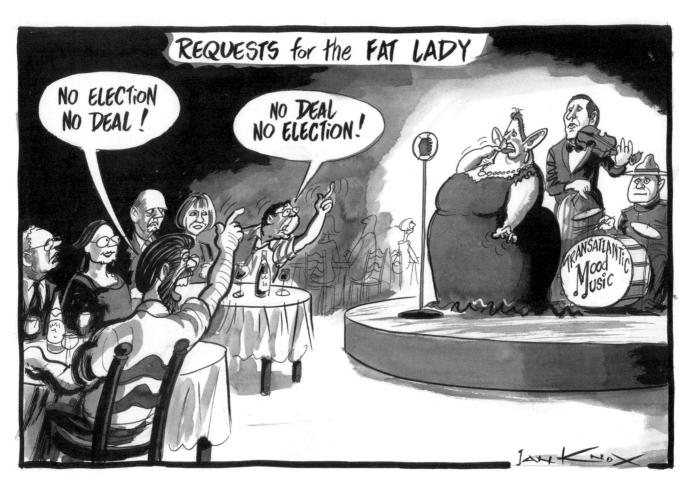

08.10.2003 Uncertainty continues over the announcement of an election. The US administration wants elections sooner rather than later and nationalists point out Blair's haste to impose democracy on Iraq while cancelling local assembly elections.

17.12.2003 Police confirm that fraudsters have attached cloning devices to cash points in Belfast's Royal Avenue and Castle Court.

02.03.2004 The Republic's government is concerned at Sinn Fein's growing political influence in the south, while the British government is apprehensive about the imminent publication of the Cory inquiry into collusion between the police and loyalist paramilitaries.

05.03.2004 George Mitchell is elected chairman of the Walt Disney Company.

06.05.2004

19.11.2004 It is suggested that a respected religious figure
would be a credible witness for decommissioning.

08.12.2004 A group of law lords rule that government policy of indefinite detention for asylum seekers is illegal. In Bogota, the attorney-general secretly overturns the acquittal of the "Colombia 3".

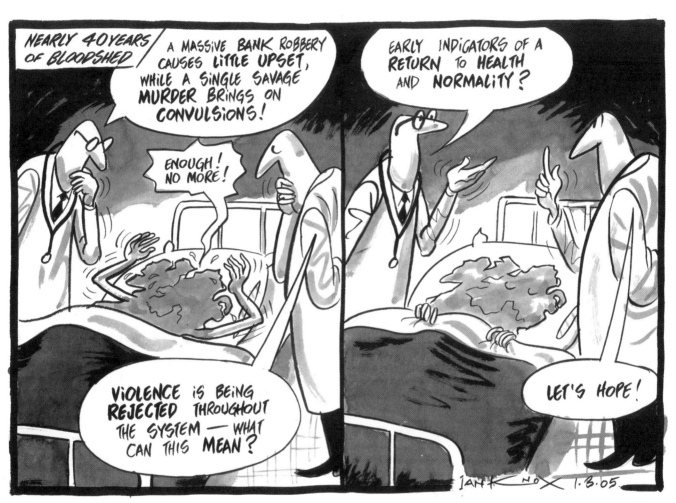

01.03.2005 The murder of Robert McCartney provokes a much greater degree of public outrage and trouble for Sinn Fein than does the Northern Bank raid.

07.05.2005 The DUP and Sinn Fein emerge from elections
as the two dominant political parties.

08.09.2001 Paisley remains unavailable for comment on the protest and attacks at the Holy Cross Girls' Primary School.

26.11.2001

01.11.2003 Michael "something of the night" Howard bids for the Conservative party leadership, while the DUP show a slide show, "David Trimble's Halloween – the new nightmare", at their election campaign launch.

THROUGHOUT MY **POLITICAL** LIFE, HOME SECRETARY, THERE HAVE BEEN THOSE WHO DISMISSED ME AS AN **INSANE, DESTRUCTIVE HATE MONGER!** — EVEN NOW THAT I AM **TOP DOG** THEY STILL VIEW ME AS UNHINGED AND **TWO DIMENSIONAL!**

INDEED!

03.12.2003

31.01.2004 Paisley attends talks at the Irish Embassy in London.

05.12.2003 Paisley publicly lambasts President Bush's special envoy Richard Haass as being "favourable to the IRA", apparently unaware that a DUP team was engaging in discussions with Haass which Peter Robinson later stressed had been "positive".

31.08.2004 Former Irish priest Cornelius Horan disrupts the Olympics men's marathon. His brother Michael describes Cornelius as having a "crazed notion about the Bible and the end of the world".

03.03.2004 Following press speculation on his increasingly frail appearance, Paisley describes journalists as "Romanists" and offers to "take a few thousand pounds off some newspapers who lied about me".

08.12.2004 Prospects for an historic political deal appear to slip away as Paisley insists on photographic evidence of IRA decommissioning.

17.12.2004 Paisley maintains that the humiliation of the IRA is as important as reassurance for unionists in his desire for photographs.

21.12.2004 Violent protests by the Sikh community forces a play "Behtzi" (dishonour) to close at the Birmingham Repertory Theatre. Meanwhile, news breaks that six Belfast libraries have been selected for closure.

12.01.2005 A series of gales sweep the North.

17.09.2005

24.11.2000 The High Court gives Martin McGuinness and Bairbre de Brun the go-ahead to challenge David Trimble's ban on them attending the North South Ministerial Council.

01.06.2002 Alex Maskey is elected the first Sinn Fein lord mayor of Belfast.

18.01.2003 The creation of preconditions for Sinn Fein to satisfy becomes competitive.

14.07.2004 Gerry Kelly sustains an arm injury while trying to deflect attacks on the army during a riot following an Orange march through Ardoyne.

16.09.2004 Sinn Fein bring the monster, pre-microchip bugging device found at Connolly House to the Leeds Castle talks.

28.01.2005 In the aftermath of the Northern Bank raid, the relationship between Sinn Fein and the British Government is frostily suspicious.

05.02.2005

15.02.2005 The beginning of the political fallout from the murder of Robert McCartney...

18.02.2005 ...and the lesser fallout from the Northern Bank raid.

19.02.2005 The Republic's government struggles to limit the damage done by speeding on the roads and the political success of Sinn Fein.

09.03.2005 The uncharacteristically inept response of the IRA to the McCartney murder undermines Sinn Fein's arguments for not joining the Policing Board.

24.09.2002 Upwards of 800 members of the ruling Ulster Unionist Council threaten to quit the Stormont administration. Trimble wards off confrontation with Jeffrey Donaldson by putting forward a more hardline motion than him, prompting the challenge that he is "now wearing Mr Donaldson's clothes".

01.02.2003 The SDLP and Sinn Fein co-sponsor a motion to officially remove the "London" from Londonderry. Trimble visits Derry and accuses the SDLP of "moral cowardice" and "crude sectarian triumphalism".

04.03.2003 A joint declaration document from the two prime ministers aims to bring about the full implementation of the Good Friday Agreement and restore the devolved institutions, but refers to demilitarisation and an amnesty for "on the runs".

05.03.2003 Trimble continues his tradition of early departures.

30.05.2003 Trimble says he won't "lift his little finger" to support the Joint Declaration until the Royal Irish Regiment's future is secured. Donaldson calls an Ulster Unionist Council meeting in a bid to formally oppose the declaration, but Trimble arranges a separate meeting of the party Executive, urging Donaldson to call his meeting off.

13.06.2003 UUP internal feuding escalates with Trimble and Donaldson facing tit-for-tat no confidence votes in their Upper Bann and Lagan constituencies.

27.06.2003 Having failed to topple their leader at the UUP Council meeting, the three rebel MPs – Donaldson, Martin Smyth and David Burnside – announce their withdrawal from the parliamentary party and refusal to accept the party whip in the Commons. The party not so much breaks for the summer as splinters for good.

06.01.2004 Jeffrey announces that he is finally going to join the DUP.

03.03.2004 Trimble withdraws from the Stormont review.

28.04.2000 The SDLP debates an internal report which paints it as "middle class and tired". Lord Gerry Fitt claims the party is far removed from the socialist ideals on which he helped found it.

20.07.2004 The DUP and Sinn Fein unite in blaming the Parades Commission for vacillation. Mark Durkan insists the commission is still the best body for dealing with the issue but lacks a clear, coherent strategy and the backbone to implement it.

18.11.2000 The advanced age of many delegates at the SDLP conference in Newcastle is pointed out to John Hume. Shortly afterwards, he steps down and Mark Durkan is unanimously endorsed as party leader.

28.07.2000 The report by Chris Patten, the last British Governor General of Hong Kong, on the future of Northern Ireland policing is so radical and comprehensive that, as a sweetener, the RUC are awarded the George Cross. Chief Constable Ronnie Flanagan receives the award. It represents "thank you and goodbye".

21.11.2000 Secretary of State Peter Mandelson describes the legislative passage of the policing bill as a "slightly bruising experience for all sides".

22.11.2000 The Police (NI) Bill clears the Commons and awaits royal assent.
Seamus Mallon criticises the bill for its lack of clarity and the vagueness of the
implementation plan.

05.10.2002 Police carry out a very public raid on Sinn Fein's offices at Stormont and arrest a number of individuals.

18.02.03 After an exchange with Manchester United boss Alex Ferguson, David Beckham appears with a bandaged left eyebrow, claiming he did it with his own boot. Hugh Orde describes the Saville inquiry into Bloody Sunday as a waste of money but later says he didn't mean "to cast doubts on the legitimacy of that inquiry" after he is criticised for his remarks.

16.07.2004 Lord Butler says that, while intelligence used to justify the war against Iraq is flawed, no one is to blame. The Morris Tribunal finds that two members of the Garda Siochana orchestrated the planting of ammunition and hoax explosives in County Donegal.

27.07.2004 A series of loyalist attacks on Catholic homes in Carrickfergus's Thomas Street area are believed to have been prompted by a Celtic poster seen hanging on a child's bedroom wall. Nine people are forced to flee the town.

28.07.2004 Peter Mandelson follows Chris Patten into the EU Commissioner's post. While Secretary of State, Mandelson sought to change the terms of the policing bill.

24.12.2004 Following the Northern Bank raid it emerges that a traffic warden had reported a white van and suspicious activity outside the bank's side door. When police officers arrived, there was no evidence of a crime.

26.03.2005 Major drug dealer Colin Robert Armstrong, whose £5-million assets are seized by the Assets Recovery Agency, turns out to have been a former full-time RUC reservist.

04.01.2005 Under the 30-year rule, previously confidential government papers are made public. However, in Belfast, actual day-by-day minutes, recording ministerial views and decisions, have mysteriously gone missing.

27.07.2005 The UVF carry out a series of daylight evictions of LVF rivals in the shadow of Garnerville police station. In Ballymena there is more vandalism of Harryville chapel.

17.08.2005 Loyalists continue daylight attacks on the few remaining Catholics in Ahoghill unhindered and apparently unseen by the police. In Gaza, the Israeli police start the eviction of Israeli settlers.

27.03.1993 In three loyalist attacks in 24 hours, the UFF murder Peter Gallagher, and injure the wife and four children of Sinn Fein councillor Gerard McGuigan. In Warrington, an IRA bomb kills three-year-old Jonathan Ball and twelve-year-old Tim Parry.

24.06.2000 Two days before the contentious "tour of the north" Orange march, the Parades Commission launches its annual report which stresses that the number of contentious marches remains low.

17.01.2001 A primed 1,000 pound bomb is discovered on the Armagh-Monaghan road.

27.06.2001 St Bernard's Catholic church in Glengormley is burned to the ground by loyalists. The congregation transfers to St Mary's on the Hill, which is in turn attacked by loyalist arsonists.

10.09.2001 In an attempt to defend the indefensible, demographics are used by Glenbryn residents in north Belfast to justify their attacks.

31.07.2002 A fire engine, stoned and put out of service by a mob at Silvio Street, is only the latest in a series of attacks on firefighters and paramedics.

26.10.2002 The Continuity IRA plants a bomb which partially explodes in Franklin Street, close to Windsor House.

07.04.2004

07.04.2004

13.05.1995 The Orange Order expresses a belief that genuine residents of the lower Ormeau Road are waiting to welcome them.

27.03.2002 The Parades Commission bans a contentious Apprentice Boys march from the lower Ormeau Road on Easter Sunday, while another contentious Apprentice Boys march is given the go-ahead.

08.07.2002 Violence erupts once again at Drumcree; once again, the Orange Order blames media attention for turning up the temperature.

09.07.2002 To everyone but the Order itself, Orange behaviour at Drumcree appears self-destructive.

19.03.2004 Unionist councillors complain about tricolours and booze at the St Patrick's Day celebrations in Belfast.

26.06.2004 The Parades Commission reverses its ban on a controversial Orange parade from a stretch of the Springfield Road in west Belfast.

09.07.2005

15.04.2000 A survey finds that over one third of 1,250 people questioned were unwilling to accept the idea of a person from an ethnic minority as a workplace colleague.

01.04.2005 Filipino nurses and foreign doctors are attacked.

23.07.2004

16.02.2002 Opposition to the visual impact of offshore windmills is expressed in North Antrim.

11.06.2003 The Irish Government begins legal proceedings in The Hague designed to force the British Government to shut Sellafield.

15.10.2003 Direct rule minister Angela Smith refuses Dungannon coursing club a licence to net hares for their annual meeting.

09.12.2003 Arguments used to justify hare coursing echo those previously employed to justify slavery.

30.06.2004 The quality of the North's water supply is criticised by EU inspectors, particularly the unregulated use of chemicals by unqualified staff at the water maintenance plants.

11.08.2004 The European Commission confirms it has begun legal action against the UK government over Northern Ireland's continuing failure to comply with sewage law.

21.08.2004 A leaked copy of a letter from Secretary of State Paul Murphy to Chief Secretary of the Treasury, Paul Boateng, shows that the Northern Ireland Office was proposing to disguise water charges by raising regional rates.

15.10.2004

27.11.2004 Developers and "tractor boy" students combine to submerge
the unique architectonic quality of the Belfast Holy Land area
in breeze-block extensions and booze.

30.03.2005

16.04.2005 Dick Roche, the Republic's Minister for the Environment, publishes the Rural Housing Planning Guidelines, removing the last meagre restrictions on ribbon development and ushering in the final conquest of bungalow blitz.

28.02.2001 The personal relationship between British and American leaders seems to intensify at moments of crisis for the US. When the press asks Bush at Camp David what unites him with the other main architect of the "War on Terror", he replies that they both use Colgate toothpaste.

31.03.2001 George Bush abandons the Kyoto Treaty, while Unionist MP Roy Beggs comes under criticism for his management of a landfill site on the Ballyrickard Road.

11.02.2003 George Bush describes the row within NATO, which threatens to derail US plans for a military invasion of Iraq, as evidence of NATO's lack of credibility. Opponents of the invasion point out that the intelligence used to compile Blair's "dodgy dossier" was more lacking in credibility.

23.08.2003

19.07.2005

04.12.2001

23.02.2002 Israeli tanks move into Gaza for the first time during the latest Palestinian uprising. A local broadcasting station is blown up and an Israeli helicopter fires at least one rocket into Yasser Arafat's Ramallah compound.

03.04.2002 Tourists and visitors are trapped in Bethlehem's Church of the Nativity by the Israeli "operation protective wall" incursion. A 65-year-old priest is killed, BBC correspondent Orla Guerin is fired on, and comedian and political activist Jeremy Hardy is caught up in violent clashes.

06.04.2002

22.04.2002 After the Stormont raid, police searches of Sinn Fein workers' homes finds nothing significant, but the perceived political objective of the searches – the end of the Assembly – is achieved. Meanwhile, Chris Patten points out that the building at the centre of the destructive invasion of Jenin by Israelis was the Land Registry, and Ariel Sharon's obsession for destroying any documents recording Palestinian ownership of land was the possible motive for the exercise.

28.01.2003 Israel clamps a three day closure on the West Bank and the Gaza Strip for its fourth election in seven years.

25.03.2003 ITN journalist Terry Lloyd is killed by "friendly fire" in Iraq.

26.03.2003

27.05.2003 The Israeli government conditionally approves a US-backed "road map" to Middle East peace, which envisages a Palestinian state by 2005. Referring to Israel's 36-year occupation of the West Bank and the Gaza Strip, Sharon is heckled by his own party hawks when he argues that "to keep 3.5 million people under occupation is bad for us and them".

26.03.2004 Tony Blair's visit to Libya coincides with the signing of a multi-million pound deal with the Anglo-Dutch oil giant Shell.

16.04.2004 Following discussions on Israel and Palestine which excluded Palestinian input, Bush states that Israel should be able to keep some settlements in any future peace agreement. He also embraces Sharon's position that Palestinian refugees should be allowed to return to a new Palestine, but not to Israel.

03.02.2001 The University of Ulster sets up an Institute of Ulster-Scots studies at the Magee Campus.

03.09.2001 Anti-Agreement unionists prevent the re-election of David Trimble as First Minister and throw the assembly into crisis.

15.11.2002 Members of the Belfast arts community boycott a gala awards dinner said to have cost £47,000 in protest at cuts to funding. Professor George Bain, Vice Chancellor of Queen's University, earmarks a number of departments for closure as part of a "restructuring" programme.

16.09.2003 On the eve of Cemetery Sunday at Carnmoney, the "Loyalist Action Force" threatens the life of Fr Dan Whyte. A 200-strong loyalist protest disrupts the service, two hijacked vehicles are set on fire, gravestones are smashed and graffiti is daubed on the chapel door. UUP councillor Ivan Hunter blames Fr Whyte for inflaming passions, citing the fact the graffiti wasn't removed as proof "that he has an agenda".

12.12.2003 Missing files and forensic evidence, as well as Establishment obstruction, severely limit the scope of Justice Barron's inquiry into circumstances surrounding the 1974 Dublin and Monaghan bombings.

28.05.2004 The Ulster-Scots musical extravaganza "On Eagle's Wing" rises phoenix-like from the ashes of its cancelled US openings to premiere at the Belfast Odyssey.

16.10.2004 The Republic fails to meets its financial commitment to UN aid.

25.01.2005 Ray Burke's appeal is less successful than that of
the IRA killers of Garda McCabe.

04.06.2005 The new City of Lisburn succeeds in getting the John Lewis group to open a store at Sprucefield shopping centre.